No Snow Day for the Brain

Kate Brown, Rebecca Hammond,
& Alex Nisbet

No Snow Day
for the
BRAIN

Kate Brown, Rebecca Hammond, & Alex Nisbet

With Illustrations by Olivia Schenck

Edited by Nancy Michael, PhD

Written as part of
Self-Healing Communities of Greater Michiana

February 2022
South Bend, Indiana

This book was written with the intention of helping everyone understand the science of the brain. You will learn that your everyday experiences change the way your brain grows; this is called neuroplasticity. We hope to show you how strong relationships are the foundation of neurobiological care and resilience. Everyone has a brain, so this science applies to everyone! Please join us, we are so glad you are here.

First paperback edition February 2022

ISBN: 979-8-9857644-4-4   (Hardcover)
ISBN: 979-8-9857644-3-7   (Paperback)
ISBN: 979-8-9857644-5-1   (eBook)

Self-Healing Communities Purpose Statement

SELF-HEALING COMMUNITIES

A Meta Leadership Coalition to Build Resilient Communities

Self-Healing Communities (S-HC) is a community change model that is rooted in an understanding of the neurobiology of trauma, healing, and human resilience. Full development and flourishing of the human brain require humans to be treated in compassionate and predictable ways. The goal of our coalition, S-HC of Greater Michiana, is to teach everyone in our community to take care of themselves and each other in a way that prioritizes caring for the nervous system. We will know we are experiencing healing in our community when everyone starts to show up and take care of themselves and each other in these ways.

Self-Healing Communities is a community coalition approach developed in response to the common question following an ACEs training: "What's next?" S-HC of Greater Michiana uses a strategy modeled after methodology implemented in Washington State across multiple municipalities and resulted in significant decreases in a number of adverse community health measures.[1] One key piece of this model is *distributed leadership*, owned not by any one organization, but owned by the community at large, with key organizations in the community serving in "Meta Leadership" roles. A second critical piece of the S-HC Model is NEAR science: the scientific evidence surrounding Neuroscience, Epigenetics, ACEs, and Resilience. Cumulatively, these disciplines help us understand how to address stress and its impacts on communities and examine the long-term effects on individuals. NEAR science also provides scientifically based methods for alleviating impact, reversing effects, and preventing future harm to individuals and communities.

---

[1] Porter, Laura. Martin, Kimberly, & Anda, Robert. (2016) *Self-Healing Communities: A Transformational Process Model for Improving Intergenerational Health.* A report commissioned by the Robert Wood Johnson Foundation. Rwjf.org

Self-Healing Communities seeks to ensure that community members and organizations have the necessary knowledge, understanding, and skills to take care of each other the way the brain and body expect. These communities are extraordinarily reflective and committed to continuous improvement. When a community takes care of its members in this way, it can be considered self-healing.

Advancing the work of S-HC of Greater Michiana requires patience and consistent continuous relationship-building across sectors, through a Trauma-Informed lens. In accordance with the original research, our primary goals are to increase the number Trauma-Informed organizations in Greater Michiana, expand PACEs Training to everyday citizens, develop and distribute materials focused on neurobiological care for people of all ages, create a community resource portal/website to access all of our S-HC resources, develop incremental data-tracking procedures, and create opportunities for the community to celebrate resilience.

Contact us at selfhealingcommunities@gmail.com.

Visit our YouTube channel (@Self-Healing Communities of Greater Michiana) to hear from the book's creators!

If you enjoyed reading this book and would like to purchase another copy, please use the following link to access our bookstore on Lulu.com:

https://tinyurl.com/no-snow-day-for-the-brain

We would especially like to thank Velshonna Luckey, Dr. Nancy Michael, and Kimberly Green Reeves for their consistent support and constructive feedback throughout the writing process. Thank you all for inspiring us to use neuroscience to serve a greater purpose.

Additional Acknowledgments

Much gratitude to Dr. Margaret Jessop, psychologist and children's author who believed in this project enough to offer feedback and take it to her authors' group. Many thanks to Stana and Niki Michael who provided critical critique through the lens of children's lived experiences. Thank you to Maryann Krasko and Kristen Brown for their thorough proofreading of this work. Completion of this book also required input and coordination across the entire S-HC team, so sincere thanks to Aysha Gibson, Karina Duffy, Carey Gaudern, and Ann Hoewing for all that you do behind the scenes to make ideas become realities.

Table of Contents

Foreword I

Chapter 1: The Snow Day 1

Chapter 2: The TV 6

Chapter 3: The Tug of War 9

Chapter 4: The Snowball Fight 13

Chapter 5: The Best Sister 17

Chapter 6: The Sledding Hill 21

Chapter 7: The Abandoned House 24

Epilogue: Pizza Party! 28

Inside the Brain:
No Snow Day for the Brain 33

The Golden Rule: Sleep! 64

Glossary 67

Reflection & Activities 75

Foreword

My name is Nancy Michael. Professionally, I'm the Director of Undergraduate Studies for the Neuroscience and Behavior major at the University of Notre Dame. Personally, I'm a daughter, sibling, wife and mother of two amazing daughters. I was a "non-traditional" graduate student with almost a decade in the workforce between my undergraduate and graduate education. During grad school, I got married and had my first daughter – at a time when I was learning SO MUCH about the brain! As I learned about how the brain works and what the brain expects from its environment – that's right, the brain actually *expects* stuff from the environment to grow up healthy – I kept wondering more and more why everyone didn't know this stuff? Throughout my education and experience, I've learned that I'm not the only one who finds the brain fascinating – excitement from strangers about brain function taught me that this knowledge should be shared with as many people as possible! It turns out that understanding how the brain works gives us all the power to do something differently; to take better care of ourselves and those we care about.

This book was created with the hope of sharing an unusual language of empowerment: the language of neuroscience. By understanding what the brain expects, we all have the opportunity to work *within* our culture, background, personal history, etc., to protect the health of our brains. How many arguments between parents and children could be avoided if we (culturally and as caregivers) just understood a little bit more about what was happening *inside* our brains?

I

The language of neuroscience teaches us that what we do and how we show up in the world _does matter so much_ in the lives of others. So, whether it's a different perspective with kids, more patience with a family member, or just being kind to strangers, understanding what the brain expects allows us to work with our own strengths, skills, and resources to better care for ourselves and the people in our lives. The familial relationships in this story do not necessarily represent _the world as it is_, but perhaps _what the world could be_ if we all intentionally created relationships that honor the brain's most foundational need for secure, consistent care. The hope for this children's book, NEAR science, and Self-Healing Communities in general, is to cultivate community understanding of the brain, especially regarding the brain's environmental expectations, so we can all be better caretakers, of ourselves and the people in our lives.

Nancy Michael, PhD

April 2022

Chapter 1: The Snow Day

Rafael woke up and jumped out of bed. The sun was shining through the window. His alarm clock read 9 am!

"Oh no!" he exclaimed. "I missed the bus! How will I get to school?"

Rafael heard a loud groan. He ran to the window and watched a snowplow clear a thick, white blanket of snow off the road. *It looks like a winter wonderland*, he thought.

"Mom, I missed the bus!" Rafael shouted down the hallway.

Maria, Rafael's older sister, heard her brother and joined him in the bedroom.

"It's okay – it's a snow day!" Maria responded excitedly. "The sidewalks and roads are completely covered, so they cancelled school!"

"Did Mom and Dad leave?" Rafael asked.

That green guy is a neuron in Rafael's brain! There are about eighty-six billion neurons (that's 86,000,000,000) in the brain! At first, Rafael's brain is upset because he thinks he missed the bus but becomes happy when he realizes that school has been cancelled.

"They just left for work," said Maria. "But we're going over to Sarah's house for lunch, and Mom said we can call them if we need anything."

"I wish we could hang out with Mom and Dad today," Rafael remarked sadly. "What are you going to do?"

Maria was not sure if she wanted to bring Rafael along, but also knew she could not leave him home alone.

"Well," Maria said, "my neighborhood friends and I might play games, or maybe even build a snowman. You should come play with us."

"Maybe!" said Rafael as he dashed around the house shouting: "No homework!"

"Mom and Dad did give us some chores, though!" Maria shouted after him. "You have to give Louis his dog food and take him outside, and I have to put away the dishes."

"Feeding Louis is easy and I will take him outside later! Now I just have to decide what to do!" Rafael declared.

Notice that Rafael and Maria's neurons have special "hair." This hair represents the neurons' dendrites. Dendrites have branches that grow and change as we learn new things. Rafael's sister, Maria, is older and more experienced than he, which is why her neuron has more complicated dendrites with more branching.

Chapter 2: The TV

Rafael's head was swirling with ideas of fun things to do now that school was canceled! Without his usual math problems and spelling quizzes, he could not decide what to do first...

His eyes darted from the board games to the backyard to the piano, then, he settled on his choice: the TV!

"Maria! I am going to watch a show!" Rafael yelled. He could not hide his smile as he thought about watching his favorite show all day long.

Maria rolled her eyes. "Fine Raf, do whatever you want! Just remember, it would be more fun to play outside with everyone else."

Rafael shrugged his shoulders. He jumped onto his coolest squishy bean bag chair and started flipping through all the TV shows and movies. Suddenly, he heard laughing and shouting outside.

As he listened closer, he started to recognize the voices!

Rafael is so excited to watch TV! However, when Rafael is sitting around watching TV, that means his neurons are sitting around all day too. They are not doing much learning, thinking, or growing!

Chapter 3: The Tug-of-War

A chorus of "Ow!" and "Got ya!" rang throughout the yard.

"Maria, is that Sarah playing outside?" asked Rafael as he looked out the window.

"It is. It looks like everyone is having a snowball fight!" Maria responded excitedly. "We should join them!"

I do want to watch TV, Rafael thought, *but it sounds like they're having so much fun outside! What should I do?*

Rafael felt like there was a tug-of-war happening inside his brain!

Rafael can't decide if he wants to stay inside or play outside, which is why he feels this tug-of-war in his brain!

A second later, he made his decision. "We should go play! Just watching them throw snowballs makes me want to throw one too," he said. It was easy for him to imagine himself out there with his friends.

As Rafael went to get his snow pants and gloves, he said quietly, "I've never been in a real snowball fight before."

Maria heard him and quickly replied, "Watch and learn."

Rafael followed her outside. The cold, crisp air hit his face as he ran off to join in on the games.

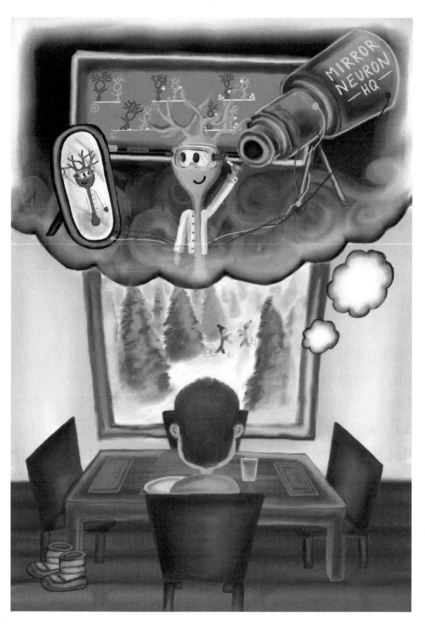

As Rafael looks out the window and sees his friends throwing snowballs, his mirror neurons (a special type of neuron) help him imagine what it would be like to throw a snowball himself. Mirror neurons help us learn things from the world around us!

Chapter 4: The Snowball Fight

As soon as Rafael made it to the backyard, he was in the middle of a big snowball fight! All the neighbors were already split into teams. Tommy and Sam, two of the big middle school kids, were making stockpiles of snowballs. Maria and Sarah started building a snow fort for their team.

"Rafael! Rafael! Come help us with this fort," they shouted.

Rafael moved as fast as he could through the thick, crunchy snow.

Am I the youngest person here? He wondered to himself nervously. Rafael was unsure if he could keep up because he had never been in a snowball fight before. Even worse, Tommy and Sam liked to make fun of Rafael for being short when he's around the bigger kids. One time, they wouldn't even let Rafael ride their skateboards because they said he was too small. Even though he knew that Maria would have his back, being the little kid made Rafael feel yucky inside.

Rafael helped Maria finish the fort just as snowballs started to fly overhead. Two groups had formed. Rafael, Maria, Sarah, Tommy, and Sam would be battling against Maria's friends from a few blocks away.

"Okay, Rafael, your job is to hide behind the wall, wait until someone isn't looking, and then throw a snowball at their leg. Don't mess up – we want to win!" Sam yelled.

"Ahh!" Rafael cried out as a snowball hit him in the leg. He picked up another snowball and threw it as hard as he could. It missed the target.

"We are losing! Come on, Rafael!" Tommy shouted. "Who even invited Rafael to be on this team anyway?"

Rafael's stomach was starting to feel more and more yucky, and his hands were a bit shaky too. His face felt warm and red.

Maria glared at Tommy. "Hey!" she said. "Either you can stop, or we both are going to have to leave."

"It's fine, Maria!" Rafael shouted. "I don't want to play anyway! I don't like being on the losing team either!"

Tommy angrily chucked a snowball at Rafael, hitting him in the face. Rafael grabbed his eye and ran the other way. He couldn't believe Tommy did that! As he wiped his eyes, the melting snow mixed with his tears.

Oh no, Rafael thought, *if anyone sees me, I will be known as the neighborhood crybaby forever!*

The yucky feeling in his stomach was spreading, and his head started to feel fuzzy.

Rafael ran inside.

Even though it is cold outside, Rafael's fears and frustrations make it feel like his brain is on fire! When your brain feels like it is on fire, it can be hard for you to understand what is happening in your body.

Chapter 5: The Best Sister

Rafael headed straight for the beanbag chair. At home, he could watch TV all day long, and nobody would make fun of him. *Maybe I should have just stayed inside.*

Wham! The door swung open. "Hey, Raf! Raf! Come back!" Maria called.

"What do you want?" Rafael said, trying to hide his tears. "I thought you were having fun with your friends."

"Um, I don't really know – I guess I just wanted to see if you're okay," Maria replied.

"Yeah, I'm fine. The snowball didn't hurt that bad," said Rafael.

"Are you sure you're okay? You're crying, so that must mean you're sad or something!"

"Well," Rafael started, "I don't feel good. My stomach feels weird, my hands are shaky, and my head hurts. But I don't want to be a crybaby.

And even though I know he's supposed to be our friend, I'm mad at Tommy for saying it's my fault we lost. But I'm also scared, I think."

Maria stared at him. She didn't really know what to say. "What do you mean?"

"Well, what if he doesn't want to be friends with me? And what if that means that nobody else wants to be friends with me either? That makes me scared! I want everyone to like me! And I was just so little compared to the big kids!"

Maria sighed and hugged Rafael.

She said, "Even though he's our friend, Tommy was mean to say those things. And you're not bad at anything – you're just younger! You were doing such a good job of keeping up with the big kids! And anyway, it's not about who wins - it's just a snowball fight. Who cares? I was having fun, and now Tommy looks silly for making such a big deal about it."

Rafael rolled his eyes and said, "You sound like Mom, Maria." Then he smiled and said, "But it's okay, now I feel better."

Rafael's brain is able to cool down as he talks to Maria. When we are with someone who makes us feel safe, loved, and accepted, we can regain our sense of calm. The loving relationship between siblings means that Maria can help Rafael's brain cool down.

"Let's go back outside," Maria said, "I think playing more games will make you feel even better."

"Hey, don't tell me what to do!" Rafael joked. "I'll go outside, but only because I want to – not because you said so!"

Chapter 6: The Sledding Hill

When Rafael and Maria returned outside, the snowball fight had ended, and all their friends were playing tag.

It's so hard to run in the snow, especially in these big boots and pants, Rafael thought.

After tag, they played hide and seek and made snow angels.

"Who wants to go sledding?" Sarah excitedly asked.

"Me!" everyone shouted together.

Rafael's legs felt very tired, and he was breathing pretty hard when he got to the top of the sledding hill. It's hard to walk uphill in the snow! The first time he went down the hill, his sled didn't even go that fast. It seemed like some of the piles of snow just slowed him down.

This isn't as fun as I thought it would be, Rafael thought. He started to feel nervous again. *What if I can't keep up?*

He realized everyone was already walking back up the hill. "Maria, wait for me!" Rafael shouted as he tried to catch up.

It was difficult to keep up with his older sister. She was walking up the hill so fast! "I'm getting tired!" He shouted again.

"Try walking in my footprints in the snow," Maria called back.

"Good idea!" He realized it was easier to walk in the snow if he walked in the footsteps that his sister and the neighbors left behind. The footsteps made a path up the hill.

Even cooler, the sleds made a track as they went down the hill. Each time someone went over the track, the track became smoother and smoother. This made Rafael go faster and faster!

"I can't wait to go again!" Rafael yelled up the hill. Rafael kept walking in Maria's footsteps, and his own footsteps made the path even clearer.

"It feels like I'm flying!" Rafael shouted as he glided down the hill another time.

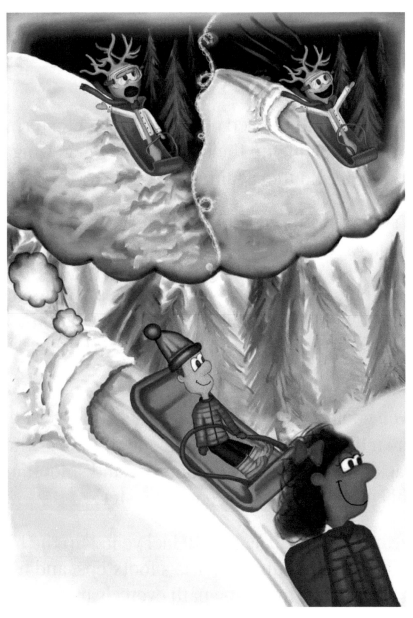

Rafael has to sled down the hill a few times before his sled can start to go really fast. In the same way, our neurons have to try a few times when learning how to do something new. Once our neurons learn how to do something, they can do it super fast!

Chapter 7: The Abandoned House

After sledding, everyone took a lunch break at Sarah's house.

Rafael took a big gulp of hot chocolate. "Ow!" he shouted. "That's really hot!" They all drank so fast they burned their tongues.

"Hey, who wants to go check out that abandoned house just past the school?" asked Sarah in between gulps of hot chocolate.

"That's kind of far away," Maria replied nervously.

"Are you sure we are allowed?" Sam asked. Legend had it that no one had lived in that house for a long time.

Maria knew that she and Rafael were not allowed to go to the abandoned house. Their parents had even reminded her before they left for work.

"I am not so sure that's a good idea," Maria spoke up.

"Oh, come on," Tommy said. "Are you scared? Don't be a baby!"

The group was quiet for a moment before Rafael spoke up. "Maria, can we go home? Louis hasn't been outside in a while, and we said we would play with him in the snow."

Maria looked back at him and nodded. "You're right," she said, "we did talk about that."

Sarah and the others headed off to the abandoned house. Maria and Rafael started their walk home.

"Thank you for helping me out back there," said Maria. "That was a good idea to come home instead of going to the abandoned house."

"You're welcome! Mom and Dad always say we're not allowed to go to that house, but I knew everyone would make fun of you if you said that." Rafael smiled to himself, proud of standing up for his big sister.

Just as the mirror neurons helped him imagine throwing a snowball, Rafael's mirror neurons help him understand how Maria is feeling. By looking at her face, he can tell that she feels nervous!

"Hey, it's Friday!" Rafael remembered. "Tonight is pizza night! I hope they bring home Roberto's Pizza Palace!"

"As long as they don't get pepperoni, I don't care where the pizza is from!" Maria laughed.

As their house came into view, Rafael looked up at his sister. "They are going to be so proud of us when we tell them about our day."

Maria smiled. "They sure will be, Raf."

Epilogue: Pizza Party

"Rafael, Maria, come on down for dinner! We brought home pizzas," called their parents.

"Yum!" Rafael shouted as he raced Maria down the stairs. He was hungry after a full day outside.

"Did you get pepperoni? I don't like pepperoni," Maria added. They rounded the corner to the kitchen and saw that Mom and Dad had brought home their favorite dinner: cheese and mushroom pizza from Roberto's Pizza Palace.

"Aw yay, you got cheese and mushroom! I wouldn't want anything else," Rafael said.

As they settled around the table, Dad asked, "How was your snow day, kids?"

"It was so fun," said Maria, smiling. "We have not had a snow day in so long, and I got to do everything I wanted outside with Raf."

Rafael and Maria are excited for their parents to come home for dinner. After a long and action-filled day, Rafael and Maria's neurons in their brains help them decide what is most important to share with the family.

28

"I learned how to throw a snowball," Rafael shared, "but I also learned how to get hit with snowballs. Tommy made fun of me for being little, which made me feel scared, but Maria stuck up for me."

"And then you helped me out!" Maria chimed in.

"When Sarah suggested going to the abandoned house, Raf could tell that I didn't want to go, so he said I needed to go home with him and take Louis out."

"We are so proud of you two," the parents said.

At the end of the night, Maria came to say goodnight to Rafael.

"Thank you for playing outside with me today." Maria gave Rafael a hug and sat on his bed. "I don't know what I would do without you."

Tomorrow might bring the melting of the snow, but just for the moment, thoughts of snowball fights, sledding, and hot chocolate swirled in their heads as they drifted off to sleep.

No Snow Day for the Brain:
Inside the Brain

A note to the reader:

This section is for the "bigger person" who is reading this book with a child. By taking the time to read this book with this child, you can become their superhero. All of us rely on bigger people in our lives to give us advice and help us through tough situations. In the future, we become the bigger people who support the next generation. The brains of children expect consistent, supportive care from bigger people around them. All young brains expect this type of care. Even when we are older, our brains still expect strong relationships with others to help us get through tough times. This guiding figure doesn't have to be just a parent or family member but can be a guardian, neighbor, teacher, babysitter, community member, or any other person who cares about and shows up for a younger person in their life. A bigger person also does not necessarily have to be an adult, and more often than not, children have a variety of bigger people in their lives who they look up to. No matter their specific role, every bigger person is vital to the health and development of a child.

Throughout the story, there were a lot of pictures of brain cells, also called neurons, doing different things as Rafael experienced his snow day. In this section, you will find deeper explanations about neuroscience throughout No Snow Day for the Brain. What is neuroscience, you might ask? Neuroscience is the study of the brain. In this book, we wanted to provide an example of the relationships that are necessary for young brains to grow up healthy, strong, and resilient. In each section, there are also resources for how to apply what you learn about brain health to real life. We hope that the following will show you how bigger people, like you, have a huge impact on the lives of younger people. We offer this "neuroscience knowledge" as another tool to add to your toolbox, strengthening the ways you can support yourself and the people in your life. By taking what we know about healthy brain development and applying it to our daily lives, we can use this understanding to better support each other and ultimately build healthier and happier families and communities.

Some brain basics:

The word "neuroscience" can feel really intimidating. We don't often talk about the brain in school, and most folks have to stay in school well beyond high school to have a chance to learn about how cool the brain actually is! But here's a secret – no matter what you've heard, it's not so hard to learn about the brain! And, if it's not clear already, we really think that understanding how your brain and others' brains work helps us A LOT when we're trying to support people, take care of ourselves, and solve problems. So, why shouldn't we share neuroscience with as many people who want to learn? That's our job here: establish some brain basics. When you understand the brain, you can better understand why we do what we do. **Welcome to your first neuroscience crash course!**

Here is an image of the brain... If you cut a human brain down the middle to split into the left and right sides, this is what you would see. The parts of the brain labeled in the picture are the parts that played a major role in how Rafael understood his experiences in the story.

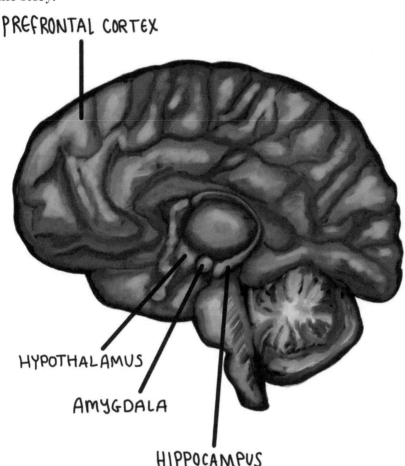

PREFRONTAL CORTEX

HYPOTHALAMUS

AMYGDALA

HIPPOCAMPUS

1. Rafael's Amygdala thinks he missed the bus

<u>What's Going on Here?</u>
Our understanding of the world is based on our previous experiences. Our brains are always active. They take in information from the world around us, process it, compare it to what we have learned before, and figure out what to do about it. When Rafael wakes up and sees that it is 9:00 am, he feels a sense of panic and stress, because his previous learning tells him he's late for school! However, when he learns that it is a snow day, he quickly calms down and starts to feel excited rather than scared. Our brains are constantly evaluating the information we receive from the world around us, but sometimes certain parts of our brains and bodies react before we have time to fully process the situation. This is why you may feel scared or nervous in an instant, before you fully understand *why* something has made you scared.

<u>Inside the Brain:</u>
In this chapter, Rafael begins to panic when he sees that the time on the clock is later than usual. Whenever we are worried or scared, a part of the brain called the **amygdala** is activated. The amygdala starts the **stress response** in our body. The stress

response is commonly known as the *fight-or-flight response*, and it gives us the feeling of a sinking stomach or a racing heart or even the feeling of warmth in our face.

The part of the brain called the **hippocampus** helps us learn, store, and remember information, while a different part of the brain called the **prefrontal cortex** helps us decide what to do, both now and in the future. After Maria tells Rafael that today is a snow day, Rafael's hippocampus (where memories are stored) and prefrontal cortex send messages to the amygdala, saying there is no need to be stressed about missing the bus. Once the amygdala receives these messages, it adjusts and starts to calm down, allowing the stress response to turn off and his body to settle down.

It is easy to feel overwhelmed by the brain and body's stress response in worrying situations. We may feel scared when we start to feel our heart racing, hands sweating, or our face becoming hot. Learning ways to notice when our bodies are showing signs of stress and learning skills to reduce these feelings can be very helpful. When learning how to manage our feelings of stress or fear, we have to realize that *fear* happens *fast*, often before we can even understand why we feel the way we do. Learning how to notice signs of stress in our bodies takes time, practice, and patience! You may have also noticed that it's hard to problem-solve, or even find words, when we're upset. Have you ever been angry or upset and someone asked you, "What's wrong with you?" or told you to "settle down and use your words"? Not helpful, right? That's because when the stress response is active, the thinking and reasoning parts of our brains are not.

The amygdala reacts so quickly because, in dangerous or threatening situations, we need to be able to *act fast*. For example, if you see a bear in the woods, your brain will determine that you need to run away. Before you even have time to think it over, your heart will start pounding faster, sending blood to fuel your muscles so that you can run away! That is why the stress response is often called the fight-or-flight response.

Calming down and problem-solving often takes longer compared to how quickly we can suddenly feel worried or scared. In order for the thinking and problem-solving parts of the brain to start troubleshooting what's going on, the amygdala has to be settled down to allow the stress response to shut off. A part of the brain called the hippocampus is responsible for calming the amygdala and ultimately shutting off the stress response. Another part of the brain called the prefrontal cortex is essential to help us problem-solve the issue at hand. Unlike the amygdala, the hippocampus and the prefrontal cortex are slower to respond and don't work well when the amygdala is on high alert. This is because the hippocampus and prefrontal cortex need to consider lots of extra information, including what we have previously experienced and stored in our memory and all the possibilities for actions and outcomes, before deciding how to react. It's like comparing how long it takes to do a simple math problem to how long it takes to solve a complex equation. The more brainpower required, the longer it takes to begin to solve the problem.

The calming down functions of the hippocampus and prefrontal cortex are complex and take time. However, with practice, you can strengthen these parts of the brain, helping you stay calm, have more patience, and be better problem-solvers for yourself and others in your life. With effort, practice, and patience, you can always build new skills, helping you learn to better regulate your emotions and discover thoughtful paths forward.

Check out the *Activities* section to learn more about how to build the strength of your hippocampus and help it learn to regulate your stress response.

2. Maria and her neuron's hair

In the image, we introduce **neurons**, extraordinarily important cells in our brains! Everything that happens in the brain, from mathematics to emotions, happens through the activity of neurons. Neurons talk to each other and send information to each other through connections called **synapses**. Each time you learn or experience something new,

more connections, or **synapses**, are created. You can also notice that Maria's **neuron** has more complex "hair" than Rafael's. The hair on her neuron represents the **dendrites,** the parts of the neuron that receive information from other neurons. Connections between neurons are created through formal education and everyday life experiences. Human relationships are essential for learning and developing new connections in our brains. We learn from the people in our life. Maria's dendrites are more complex because she is older and has had more time to create brain connections as she learns about the world.

Inside the Brain

Rafael looks up to Maria, especially when their parents are not home. She becomes the **bigger person** that he relies on. Parents or caregivers are not the only ones who can serve as this "bigger person" for a child. Siblings, teachers, and neighbors can all function in this role for those that are younger. Being a "bigger person" allows younger people to feel safe and secure in stressful or new situations. A "bigger person" also models how smaller people should react to events and manage new situations. For example, when Rafael realizes it is a snow day and doesn't know what to do next, he looks to Maria for guidance.

The importance of bigger people, and our relationships to others, begins at birth and continues throughout our lives. Infants need around-the-clock care to survive; as human infants we will literally die without consistent and responsive care from bigger people in our lives. Relationships with caregivers are so necessary for the survival of infants and children; our brains are actually obligated to turn to and attach to the bigger people in our lives. This is why bigger people have a significant influence on how our brains develop and what connections form in our young brains.

Just as Rafael's worry about missing the bus activated his amygdala and stress responses, babies become stressed when they perceive threatening situations. Infants don't have the words to say, "I'm hungry" or "I'm cold," but their brains detect those feelings and recognize those feelings as threats. When infants cry, it's because their body is stressed. Infants and children rely on the experience and problem-solving abilities of the bigger people in their lives to offer the food that will solve the issue of hunger or the blanket or snuggles that solve the issue of cold. Children's brains, even as infants, actually *expect* a responsive caregiver to pick them up when they cry and soothe them until they feel better. This responsive care helps infants and children understand that they're cared for, and that they aren't in danger. Over time, through responsive, consistent care, young brains learn that they are safe and that there will be someone to calm them down when they are in need. As children are comforted by a bigger person, they learn how to comfort themselves and others in the future.

Our brains learn and develop best when we feel safe. Relationships with bigger people are necessary even as we get older. While older children and adults might not need the constant care of infancy, humans of all ages need to feel safe and trust that they can rely on people in their lives.

3. Technology and the Brain

What's Going on Here?

If Rafael had chosen to spend the day watching TV instead of playing with his neighborhood friends, his brain would be less active. The picture shows that the brain is far less active and therefore our neurons make fewer connections when we are passively using technology compared to when we are engaging with the real world. The time we spend looking at screens takes away from other important interactions and activities that are necessary for healthy brain development. Remember, one of the main ways we build brain connections is through our interactions with others and the world around us.

Inside the Brain:

Technology affects a child's brain differently at each developmental stage. During early childhood, little brains work super hard to learn as much as they can about the world around them - from learning to walk and talk, to eventually learning how to share their thoughts and feelings. As little brains explore the world, they make millions of new connections every day! Remember, another name for these connections is *synapses*. In fact, the Harvard University Center on the Developing Child estimates that during the first two years of life, little brains make up to one million new synapses per second! At this young age, the

40

brain learns best by exploring the world with other humans, especially through the consistent care and mentorship of bigger, more experienced humans. It's clear that what small children are exposed to can have a powerful impact on which synapses are formed!

This knowledge about brain development, synapse growth, and learning informs many of the guidelines and restrictions of technology use for young children. A child's age makes a *big* difference in how technology will impact their brain development. In order to learn from technology, the brain has to be more developed. Infant and toddler brains aren't developed enough to learn from technology. In fact, the American Academy of Pediatrics recommends that no screens be used before age two. Younger brains generally don't learn well from technology and still rely on a bigger person to help them understand what the technology is trying to teach them... so it's really more like the technology is teaching the bigger person and then the bigger person teaching the smaller one.

As a child grows older and enters middle childhood (ages 4-10), their brains may be mature enough to start using technology for learning purposes. However, at this age, the danger of technology is that screen time may replace other critical activities necessary for healthy brain development, such as physical activity and interacting with peers or adults. The reality is that technology isn't going anywhere and often can be really helpful, so it is important for us bigger people to learn how to engage with technology in ways that support healthy brain development and healthy use habits. It is crucial to find opportunities for social interaction and physical movement, especially in a world where it is so easy to turn to technology instead of peers for entertainment, connection, and support!

4. Mirror Neurons

What's Going on Here?

In this scene, when Rafael runs to the window and watches his peers throw snowballs, **mirror neurons** in his brain are activated as they recognize the throwing motions. In our brains, mirror neurons actually mirror the activities of others and allow for our brains to learn by *watching* others. As Rafael watches his peers, he comments, "Just watching them throw snowballs makes me want to throw one too!" Mirror neurons

are specific brain cells that are activated when you watch someone perform a particular action *and* when you perform that action yourself.

Inside the Brain:

Mirror neurons were first discovered by accident. Neuroscientists were measuring brain activity in monkeys. A monkey was undergoing a brain experiment when a researcher decided to eat a snack. Suddenly, the computer program measuring the monkey's brain activity went nuts! The researchers investigated further and found that some brain regions and neurons become active even just by watching the actions of others! These **mirror neurons** become active while both observing the actions of others and acting out the same behavior. Rafael's 'snowball' mirror neurons will activate both when watching his friends out the window and when he starts playing with them in Chapter 4.

Studies of mirror neurons help us understand and explain how we can learn through watching others. Learning through observation is an important part of childhood development and highlights not only the importance of caretaker involvement, but also setting a behavioral example of what we want to see in smaller people's behaviors. Kids learn from everything we do! Later in the story, mirror neurons will help explain how Rafael recognizes that his sister does not want to go with her peers to the abandoned house.

5. Tug of War: Watch TV or Play with Friends

What's Going on Here?

In this picture, Rafael is choosing between two different tempting options.

Option #1: TV is fun! As we all know, watching TV can be exciting and engaging. Plus, Rafael is usually only allowed to watch TV after doing his homework, which makes this opportunity to watch TV all day even more exciting!

Option #2: On the other hand, playing with friends is exciting and engaging, and also activates our brains in new and exciting ways that we don't get from TV. As explained below, the human brain loves social interaction due to the strong communication between two brain chemicals called **dopamine** and **oxytocin.**

The neuron tug-of-war in the picture represents the competing rewards (TV time vs. time with friends) in Rafael's brain. Ultimately, playing with his friends wins out over TV time. This makes sense because brains, especially young brains, are wired to prioritize human relationships and social acceptance. Remember, the danger of screen time is not so much the screen or the technology itself, but that it displaces other activities that are essential for healthy brain function, such as physical activity or socializing.

44

Inside the Brain:

Dopamine is a **neurotransmitter** - a chemical released by neurons to send signals to other neurons - and it is released in response to rewarding behaviors, such as eating chocolate or making friends. Dopamine's job in the brain is to tell the brain to "do that again!". In other words, if there are certain actions that lead to getting an extra piece of chocolate, or making a new friend, the release of dopamine helps your brain learn what you did in order to get that positive outcome again in the future. The release of dopamine in various parts of the brain drives the desires for both social interaction and screen time.

Regarding Rafael's *Option* #1: Digital technology, especially screens, takes advantage of the brain's natural dopamine function. For example, many television programs, computer games, and phone apps are intentionally designed to activate dopamine release so that we stay engaged with the technology platform. Technology, such as television, video games, and social media, aims to keep us engaged in a few ways. First, the screen images are constantly changing and moving between scenes or ideas, thus continuing to provide new things to look at and pay attention to. Second, storylines with cliffhangers, video games with level-up incentives, and social media with "likes" are just a few ways that media and technology companies have found to stimulate dopamine release, using the brain's natural reward signal to reinforce our use of technology.

It is easy to think of this as technology 'hacking' our brains; by taking advantage of our dopamine system, technology keeps us interested and using virtual platforms, even if we know that it would be better to go outside or play with a friend. It is important to acknowledge that most screen technology is not designed with healthy brain development or function in mind.

Regarding Rafael's *Option* #2: Social interaction is especially rewarding because it combines the power of two different neurotransmitter systems. The first is the **dopamine system**, which we talked about above. The second system is the **oxytocin system.** Oxytocin is a neurotransmitter that is released during social interaction, and recent research has discovered that oxytocin release in social situations actually makes the brain release dopamine too! It's the combination of both dopamine and oxytocin that makes human social behavior so rewarding and reinforcing for us. This partnership of oxytocin and dopamine in our brains helps us understand why we are motivated to seek out social interactions, why they feel so good, and explains why humans are such social creatures!

Our early life experiences with *how* bigger people care for us establish the brain connectivity for our oxytocin-dopamine systems; these experiences create the foundational brain function that will drive how we engage with and attach to others throughout our lifetimes. Our social relationships as children teach us how to care for others and engage socially as teenagers and adults. With this in mind, we can have a deeper understanding of why it is so critical to prioritize social interactions and close relationships while children are young. As bigger people, it's our responsibility to show smaller people how to have loving and social relationships so that our actions teach them what it means to be cared for and loved.

6. Stress Activation and Caregiver Comforting

What's Going on Here?

In this part of the story, Rafael gets more and more worked up as his frustrations increase. From the beginning, he is nervous about being the youngest kid at the snowball fight. His tummy feels yucky because his stress system has been activated. Then he performs poorly in the snowball fight, just as he feared. Not meeting expectations (such as a teammate's expectations that you will perform well) can be a reason for stress. To make things worse, Rafael's own teammate makes fun of him for his poor performance. Understandably, it is stressful not to 'fit in' or be the youngest one on the team. Not being accepted by our peers is a common source of stress at all ages!

In the pictures, Rafael's stress is shown through a neuron on fire. In order to calm down, Rafael's neuron needs some support from someone who makes him feel safe, like his big sister Maria! This positive and comforting response from

47

Maria helps turn off Rafael's stress response. As Maria helps Rafael process the situation, he knows that everything will be okay. As Maria comforts Rafael, he feels safe and accepted, his stress system turns off, and their support for one another strengthens their attachment because of the release of oxytocin and dopamine!

Inside the Brain

Stress is one of the most common and well-known emotions felt by humans. Various life events can activate the stress response, such as surprises, fears, or a lack of care. Stress can occur in the body whenever there is a difference between what we expect to happen and what actually happens. Events like moving to a new school can feel stressful because our brains don't know how to predict what's coming. Even though a move might be good and exciting in the end, it's important to know that we can also feel stress in situations of *uncertainty* or not knowing what's coming.

Two key brain regions involved in stress are the **amygdala** and the **hypothalamus.** You may remember we talked about the amygdala earlier. The amygdala's job is to help us navigate our emotional world and is particularly good at detecting threats in our environment. If the amygdala detects a threat, it will talk to another part of the brain called the hypothalamus. The hypothalamus is then responsible for creating the physical sensations we associate with being stressed, like a rapid heartbeat, sweaty hands, or a hot face.

Not all stress is bad, and some stress is even good. Manageable stress, with people to support us nearby, helps our brains and bodies learn how to get through stressful periods on our own. However, it's easy for our stress to get too high. Stress that's too high can easily lead to over-emotional reactions to everyday events, such as difficulty getting along with a co-worker or struggles in romantic and social relationships. This happens because when we are exposed to elevated stress for too long, our stress system shuts down the reasoning parts of our brains, making it difficult to process and regulate stress. Given what we know about childhood brain development, the stress environment has particularly powerful effects on how children's brains develop. In both visible and invisible ways, our childhood environment has a large impact on how we grow and develop all throughout our lives.

No life is without stress, so it's important for us all to remember that stress is not always harmful. In fact, an optimal stress level can be beneficial to success in work, problem-solving, and socializing. What becomes more important than the stressful experience itself is our *response* to stress. It's the difference between being angry with a family member and 1) yelling at them in the heat of the moment or 2) stepping away to calm down and get some perspective before coming back for a calmer conversation. As bigger people, how we handle our stress becomes the model for the smaller people in our lives. If we can help smaller people learn how to process their stress and respond to stressful situations in constructive ways, their stress can lead to **resilience**.

Resilience is not the absence of stress, but the ability to manage stress without it overwhelming us; we are resilient when we have the skills to respond to hard situations in positive ways. Thankfully, resilience is natural to the human experience. It just needs practice! Life will always have its ups and downs, and learning how to manage our stress starts in childhood. We can help children develop resilience by practicing and improving our own stress management, and no matter how old we are, we can always learn new strategies to help us manage stress! Showing smaller people examples of strong, trusting relationships is also a critical part of modeling positive stress management behaviors. Be sure to

7. Learning

What's Going on Here?

In this scene, Rafael finds it hard to walk up the hill in the snow at first. However, he learns that if he steps in his sister's footsteps, then it is much easier to walk up the hill. She has already made a path in the snow. The first time Rafael sleds down the hill, his sled goes slow! There is no clear path for the sled to go down the hill. But as he continues sledding, repeating his trips up and down the hill, a clear path begins to

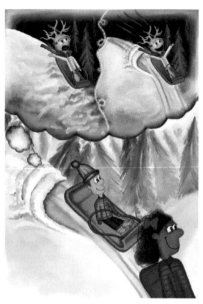

develop. Once there is a path to follow, the trips up the hill are accomplished with ease and the sled slides down the hill faster and faster.

Inside the Brain:

Remember, **neurons** are the basic building blocks of the brain, and they communicate with each other by forming connections (called *synapses*). Relationships with others, like the relationship between Rafael and Maria, help build these connections. Remember how the hair of Maria's neuron had more complex branching? It's because Maria has had many more years of experience than Rafael. Her neurons have grown more branches and more connections to each other during these experiences. This helps her understand the world and to develop skills like problem-solving. Rafael was able to learn from Maria because she had

51

experience *and* was paying attention to her little brother. The skills of bigger people are built into the connections in their brains. This is another reason why it's so important that bigger people take the time to teach smaller people. We don't learn simply because we get older. We learn because bigger people pass on what they have learned to smaller people by the examples they set, the ways they treat others, and how they engage with smaller people.

We can probably all recall that trying something new can sometimes feel scary, intimidating, and even frustrating. That's because the first time we try something new, the brain doesn't have the connections it needs between neurons to be able to do the new thing. With repetition, effort, and guidance, over time the neurons in our brains grow and develop these connections. Just like Rafael struggled climbing the sledding hill the first time, we all have experience with the challenges that can come along while trying to learn something new. Depending on what we're being asked to do and the other experiences we might draw on to help us, learning can often be a slow process.

The most important thing to remember in these moments of challenge is that we have to try. After we try things a few times, our neurons start to figure out how to communicate in new patterns, growing new branches and new connections with other neurons. Once neurons have practiced talking to each other in new patterns, tasks that used to take a lot of effort begin to feel a lot easier and tend to go much faster. The reason behind this is that your brain is actually changing – building new structures to support this new learning and skill! Just like building a new bridge takes time, effort, and persistence, building new connections in your brain does too. It's often easier to learn how to build a bridge by working with and learning from someone who has experience and has been successful at building bridges before.

In general, no matter what we are learning, our brains prefer and learn much better by being taught by someone else. When we are young, learning from someone else is a requirement of our brains. As we watch others, we are guided by their experience and can learn through observation. These connections become much more stable in our brains and become easier and easier to use, which allows us to do things faster and faster as well as add more skill or complexity to what we are learning. Just like sledding down the hill for the tenth time is easier and faster than the first time, neurons build and learn to follow a path of communication that is smooth - with no bumps of snow in the way! Remember, our brains learn through experience. In totally new situations that we've never experienced before, our brains don't have any existing connections that will help us in these moments and don't know which new paths to create. This is why the lessons we learn from bigger people are so important! It is through both lessons from others and our own experiences that our brains learn which connections to make. Like Rafael following in the footsteps of Maria, our neurons follow pathways that are formed from our experiences in life and those who are there to guide us through.

8. Mirror neurons, part 2

In this scene, Rafael utilizes his "Mirror Neuron HQ" to recognize Maria's feelings so that he can react as a loving brother and also help his sister "save face" in front of her friend. When Maria is caught between wanting to go with Sarah towards the abandoned house and knowing that it might be a bad idea, she feels uneasy. Her emotions show through her body language and are quickly recognized by Rafael. Utilizing his mirror neurons again, Rafael recognizes that Maria feels an uneasy tension about going to the abandoned house.

Rafael's brain *mirrors* the emotions he sees in Maria's face to understand that his sister is in trouble. In order to stick up for Maria, he quickly asks her if they can go home. In this scene, the lightbulb represents Rafael's awareness that his sister is making a hard decision. Rafael sees his sister's body language, knows that they are not supposed to go to the house, and steps in to help out his sister.

Inside the Brain:

Rafael's character demonstrates the remarkable ability for human brains, even young human brains, to quickly recognize emotions in others. Even with just a few years of experience, small children have had enough experience to recognize emotions in others and can respond accordingly. Scientists believe that the mirror neuron system is not only important for learning new skills (like throwing a snowball), but also a crucial component of human empathy: our ability to understand the emotions of others. In this story's example, the mirror neurons in Rafael's brain recognize the complexity of what Maria is feeling; she is uncomfortable going to the abandoned house but wants to do what her friends are doing. Our mirror neurons can be so good at detecting others' emotions that, in many cases, we start to feel something similar. In our story's example, Rafael can feel some of the same tension that his sister is experiencing.

Our ability to recognize and respond to the emotions around us develops from an early age, and as social creatures our own brains are constantly evaluating the emotions of those around us. The pathways in our brains that help our mirror neurons talk to each other are also influenced by important chemical messengers such as **oxytocin**. The information that Rafael sees is combined with his knowledge of *why* Maria feels uneasy - their parents don't want them going to the abandoned house. Without the important context of their family rules (don't go to the abandoned house!), Rafael might not understand Maria's emotions. Our emotions are constantly informed by our environment in combination with our previous learning. We all have different experiences, so sometimes it's easy for us to miss cues or misinterpret the cues of others, because we use our own experiences to help us understand what others around us might be thinking or feeling. At our core, we are social creatures, so no matter our experiences, our brains are always trying to navigate our social relationships and figure out where we fit in the world. Our mirror neuron system is an essential part of social navigation. So, the next time you recognize

9. Executive Functioning and Habits

As Rafael heads down to dinner, his brain is ready to reflect upon the day. Throughout our experiences, our brains are constantly noticing familiar surroundings and routines. In this case, the family habit of reflecting at dinner has activated Rafael's brain to prepare him to share details about his day.

Inside the Brain:

As you might recall, a lot happened during Rafael's day, so there is a lot of competing "chatter" in his head for what he wants to share with his family first! This is a perfect example of how **executive processing** allows our brains to sort through a variety of possible responses and pick out the most relevant story to share. Executive processing refers to the processes that help us 'think' about what actions to take or things to say amidst various possible options. Our brains are constantly receiving many signals from our environment, our body, and our memory. Our executive function processes help us pay attention to only the most important information, such as sticking up for your sister or learning to throw a snowball.

Context is the information about a setting or event that allows us to understand what is going on. We learn about new contexts every day, and we notice small *clues* to help us understand the

57

broader context. In this final scene, it is dinner time and this context clue tells Rafael's brain that it's time to get ready to share his day. The lightbulb in this image represents the recognition of the context clue that cues dinner time, reflecting on the day and sharing stories of the day's happenings.

With a little bit of reflection, every experience can be important for learning. This new learning for Rafael is shown through his neuron growing more complex dendrites. Every moment we observe context clues, they help us understand how to act in that situation. This context clue of dinner tells Rafael's brain that he is safe and with people that love him, allowing his brain to activate his hippocampus to reflect and sort through the events of the day, engage his amygdala to help process the emotions of the day and his prefrontal cortex to choose which stories to share first.

Each decision we make is informed by the brain's control centers, such as the prefrontal cortex and hippocampus. Executive function centers help you hold and manipulate information, practice self-control, and adapt to changes or obstacles. Just like a muscle, **the neurons in these centers grow with repeated practice and their processing power gets stronger**. Regions such as the hippocampus and prefrontal cortex are hugely important in helping us consciously think of multiple pieces of information at once and make decisions. Rafael is engaging his executive functioning as he sits at the table and weighs what to share first! Executive functioning can be practiced by anyone; check out the activities and reflection questions below to learn more!

Reflecting with others can be a good way to process emotions, think about what has happened, and ultimately, feel better about the events of the day. If something upsetting has happened, talking about it can help your brain process it.

The Golden Rule: Sleep!

The story starts with Rafael waking up in a start, thinking he's missed the bus. So, while not really a big part of the story, this little bit of neuroscience is essential for all readers to understand. No matter what you're dealing with, sleep is vital to learning in school, problem-solving at work, managing stress, helping others in your life manage their stress, or responding to a mental health problem.

It's not that we don't like sleep, but as a community, we just don't get enough. In fact, a lot of us use our lack of sleep as a badge of honor or a symbol that we're working harder than others or having more fun than others. Does this sound familiar to anyone:

- "I was up so late working on that project, I only got five hours of sleep!"
- "There's so much going on at work right now, I just can't get to bed on time."
- "We didn't get back from the game until like 4 AM!"

As bigger people, it is up to us to model healthy sleep habits for the smaller people around us.

No matter our social or family practices around sleep, neuroscience teaches us that we cannot develop a healthy brain without the right amount of sleep! And this applies to both kids and adults! Sleep is absolutely necessary for our brains to store memories over the long-term, a process called long-term memory consolidation. So, guess what, not sleeping the night before an exam or big project is actually the opposite of helpful for our learning! During the day, our neurons are really active, and just like our muscles need some rest after they work hard, the neurons in our brains do too. When we sleep, our brains can clear out the junk that neurons produce while they're working during the day. Just like you need to take the trash out of the house, your brain needs to clear the junk out of the way.

Sleep also helps us process our emotions from the day. Scientists think this is why dreams can be so crazy - we think that dreams are the brain's way of sorting through all of the emotional ups and downs we experience during our waking hours. Have you ever had something really embarrassing or hurtful happen during the day and then some version of that same event shows up in your dreams? Have you ever noticed that over time, that emotional intensity seems to fade? Scientists think we can thank our dreams for that help! If we're not getting enough sleep, we aren't getting the benefits of sleep either.

Check out the chart on the next page to do a quick self-check to see how your sleep stacks up! Can you take on a friendly challenge with some people you care about to see if you can hold yourself to healthier sleep habits?

Sleep Chart:

Age Group		Recommended hours of sleep per day
Newborn	0-3 months	14-17 hours
Infant	4-12 months	12-16 hours per 24 hours (including naps)
Toddler	1-2 years	11-14 hours per 24 hours (including naps)
Preschool	3-5 years	10-13 hours per 24 hours (including naps)
School Age	6-12 years	9-12 hours per 24 hours
Teen	13-18 years	8-10 hours per 24 hours
Adult	18-60	7 or more hours per night
	61-64	7-9 hours
	65 and older	7-8 hours

Adapted from www.cdc.gov/sleep

Glossary

Note: These terms are not in alphabetical order, but are meant to be read in the order they are listed because they build on each other.

These first five words pertain specifically to the structure of the neuron. Check out the image on the next page to help visualize what a neuron looks like!

Neuron: Also called a *nerve cell,* a neuron is the basic unit/building block of the brain and nervous system.

Dendrites: The part of the neuron that receives messages from other neurons; in our book they are represented by the hair of our neuron characters.

Axon: The part of the neuron that sends information to other neurons; in our book, they are represented by the legs and feet of our neuron characters. Axons extend from their neurons like a long string that stretches over long distances. Axons are the part of a neuron that sends messages to communicate with other neurons. Axons from one neuron release a chemical signal to "talk to" the dendrites of other neurons. Like the roots of a tree, axons branch many, many times in places we can't see. Because of this branching, one neuron is able to send messages along its axons and "talk to" many other neurons at the same time.

Neurotransmitter: The chemical signals that are released by axons are called *neurotransmitters.* Neurotransmitters are the chemical signals in our brains that communicate feelings, emotions, thoughts, and behaviors. They are constantly being released and received by neurons in our brains through a small space between axons and dendrites called a *synapse.*

Synapses (neural connections or brain connections): Axons of one neuron and the dendrites of another don't actually touch one another, but are separated by a small space called a *synapse.* Remember, neurons "talk to" each other by sending chemical signals from the axon of one neuron to the dendrite of another neuron across a small space called a synapse.

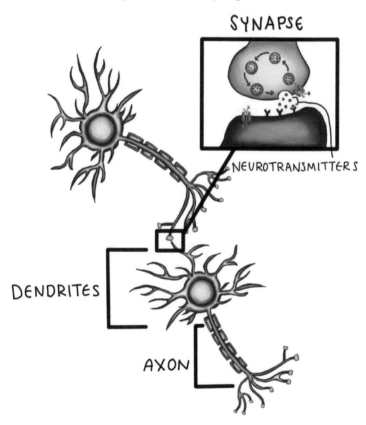

Oxytocin: A neurotransmitter that is essential for creating feelings of attachment with other people in our lives. The attachment relationships we experience with "bigger people" when we are young children help lay a foundation for the relationships we will have throughout the rest of our lives. Scientists think that oxytocin is responsible for our experiences of feelings like trust, altruism, and community.

Dopamine: A neurotransmitter that's responsible for reinforcing our behavior. For example, when we do something that earns us a hug or a good grade or the positive attention of someone we look up to, our positive experience in the world triggers a big release of dopamine that helps our brains learn to "do that again!" In experiences with negative outcomes like getting in trouble, disappointing someone we care about, or not doing well on our schoolwork, the negative experience in the world triggers a *decrease* in the amount of dopamine in our brains. This decreased dopamine signal helps our brains to learn to try something different the next time we're in a similar situation

The power couple – oxytocin and dopamine: If oxytocin helps us feel close and safely attached to other people, and dopamine helps us learn what and what not to do, the two of them together create a powerful cocktail to reinforce positive relationships in our lives. The presence of caring people in our lives makes our brains release oxytocin. The presence of social oxytocin makes the brain release dopamine, telling our brains to "do this social stuff again!" Humans, particularly young children, cannot survive without consistent, supportive care, so our brains are *hard-wired* to not only expect, but reinforce caring relationships. **Prefrontal cortex:** This brain structure is located right behind our forehead. It is also the last part of the brain to fully develop. The neurons in the prefrontal cortex get information from all over the brain and are responsible for lots of tasks like making decisions, deciding what to pay attention to, planning for the future, and problem-solving. These skills are often talked about as "executive function". Any time we have to "reason through" something or keep information in our heads to solve a problem, the prefrontal cortex is hard at work. While these things might seem easy to do, something like planning for the future takes a tremendous amount of brain power and lots of energy over a long period of time! As we've all probably noticed, when we're stressed, tired, have too many big feelings or are just overwhelmed, our prefrontal cortex and executive function skills don't work as well. It turns out our stress can actually inhibit our prefrontal cortex.

Hippocampus: A brain structure that plays an essential role in learning, memory, and navigating our way around the world. The neurons in the hippocampus get information from all kinds of different places in the brain to help us learn about, remember, and successfully navigate through the external world. Because we are humans and humans are dependent on each other, when higher levels of oxytocin and/or dopamine are around, we are able to learn about our world and each other with greater ease.

Amygdala: A brain structure that helps us figure out our emotional world. In addition to helping us figure out all emotions, the amygdala is really important for helping our brains determine threats in the world. Once our brains learn that a certain person, place, or action is associated with a threat, the amygdala changes the neurons it talks to in order to activate the fight-or-flight stress response. The fight-or-flight response helps us protect ourselves when we sense danger in our environment.

Stress Response (also known as *the fight-or-flight response*): The body's emergency reaction system. Through relationships and experience, our brains learn about our environment constantly. When our brains detect something we've learned to be threatening, the amygdala talks to a part of the brain called the hypothalamus. The hypothalamus works directly with other body systems to change things like heart rate, blood pressure, and breathing in order to arm our bodies to face the threat in our environment. The stress response also leads to the release of cortisol and adrenaline (sometimes called epinephrine - confusing, we know!) into the bloodstream, preparing the body for action against the threat.

Hypothalamus: the part of the brain that activates the *sympathetic nervous system* to change things like our heart rate and blood pressure to prepare the body for *fight*-or-*flight.*

Stressor: Any circumstance that activates the body's stress response. Life has never been "stress-free," and it even turns out that a moderate amount of stress in the presence of protective factors can be good and can lead to resilience. Stress becomes problematic when the stress system is activated too frequently or too intensely, and/or in the absence of protective factors; this kind of stress can be referred to as chronic or "toxic stress."

Mirror neuron: A neuron that is active both when we make a particular movement and when we watch someone else make the same movement. Scientists think that our mirror neuron system is responsible for why watching others do a task before we try it is so helpful for our learning. Some research suggests that mirror neurons are part of our neural system for empathy.

Protective factor (bigger person): Someone in a child's life who provides a sense of safety and direction. Because the young brain is hardwired to look to older people for safety and security, it's essential for healthy brain development that young people have older, bigger people to turn to for help or guidance. This bigger person can serve as a *protective factor*, or a buffer against the stress that a child might experience. All humans need relationships; the relationships that children have with "bigger people" help them develop the foundational brain connections that will help them succeed throughout their life.

Resilience: The ability to respond to present and future challenges in sustainable and effective ways. It entails coping well and adapting to challenging conditions. As mentioned earlier, some stress is actually good; when protective factors can buffer chronic stressors, unmanageable stress becomes manageable 'buffering.' However, a person's nervous system and overall health are most threatened when presented with prolonged, frequent, or intense stress. This highlights the need for strong, consistent, and supportive relationships in our lives because these relationships serve as our most valuable resource when managing the stressors of life. From this perspective, resilience does not arise from the absence of stress but through building individual and social capacity in the presence of a healthy amount of stress. As we develop effective coping strategies, we build the capacity to keep high levels of stress from impacting our nervous system and health — this increased capacity is *resilience.*

Learning how to treat people: In our brains, the process of learning occurs when messages frequently get sent from one neuron to the next; as this happens, new connections, or synapses, begin to form. At a certain point, the connections in the brain become so solidified that we are able to do the behavior without even thinking about it. Young brains are constantly making new connections as they learn new things about the world around them. The most important way young brains learn about the world is by *watching the people around them.* How bigger people treat other bigger people and how bigger people treat smaller people become the most important experiences that young brains use to form the foundational connections in their brains.

Learning who we want to be: One of the biggest things that we can learn from neuroscience is that two of the best ways for young brains to learn are by *watching the people around them* and *doing with others.* How we were treated and the experiences we had when our brains were young have a powerful influence on how we treat others as we grow. Some of us who had highly positive experiences when our brains were young have all of the brain connections and synapses to be strong protective factors for other people in our lives. Others of us also carry around a lot of hurt from stuff that happened a long time ago. We might not think about it a lot or think about it ever, but this hurt can sneak up on us unexpectedly and show up in how we treat others, and in this way we can pass hurts from the past onto young brains in our lives now. In this way, hurt can cross into future generations and become *transgenerational.* **The most amazing thing about neuroscience is not only understanding the brain, but understanding that we have the ability to change our brains!**

We have the ability to change our brains no matter how old we get (so, don't believe anyone who says, "you can't teach an old dog new tricks"!). Changing our brains takes time, patience, and lots of that prefrontal *executive function*, but we can do it. By learning about our own emotions, how to talk about what we need from others, and manage our own stress, we can actively take part in becoming the best protective factor we can be – for ourselves and for all those people we care about!

Reflection questions, activities, and more!

Amygdala Activation and Deactivation
Reflection Questions:
- How does your body feel when you are scared? How does it feel when you are worried or stressed? *You can check off or circle feelings from the list below.*
    - Thumping or racing heart (a heart that feels heavy or like it is beating fast)
    - Feeling sick to your stomach, like you might throw up
    - Stomach pains
    - Chest pain or a tight chest
    - Trouble breathing, feeling like you are breathing too fast or like it is hard to breathe
    - Feeling warm or sweaty
    - Headaches
- What are some ways that help you feel calm when you are stressed or scared? How do other people help you feel calm?

Action steps and activities:
- <u>Breathe</u>. Breathing is a great skill to practice when you are not stressed because it becomes a learned skill that is much easier to use when stressed. It also facilitates self-regulation which prevents the stress response to begin with. The next time you are worried or someone you know is worried, you can implement these breathing strategies in the moment, which can help calm down some of the feelings of the body. If you are doing this with a younger human, try doing the breathing exercises together.
    - Square breath (Breathe in through your nose for 3 seconds, hold for 3 seconds, out through your mouth for 3 seconds, hold for 3 seconds)
    - Deep belly breathing (i.e., tummy breathing)

- Focus on using your senses to ground you. Remember, the brain is constantly taking in information and processing it. Focus on the area around you to redirect your attention.
  - Notice 5 things you can see, four things you can feel, three things you can hear, two things you can smell, one thing you can taste.
  - If you are helping a younger human, try asking them, "What are five things you can see?", etc. and have them answer out loud

- Get curious about why. Sometimes we don't understand why we feel a certain way, we just feel it in our body. When this happens, it can help us to learn to take a minute and think about why we are feeling this way. *Older, safe people can help younger people do this.*

- Glitter jar craft. Try the glitter in the jar activity to help understand what happens in the brain when the amygdala is activated. Materials:
  - Water bottle or glass/plastic jar, mostly filled with water
  - Multicolored glitter or beads of several colors

  Instructions for glitter jar:
  - Have kids choose three colors of beads/glitter to represent behaviors, thoughts, and feelings
  - Add a few pinches of each color glitter to the water bottle and seal the bottle tightly

  Explain that the water bottle represents our brains, and the glitter represents the thoughts/feelings/behaviors that our brains process. Ask what sorts of things would cause their model brain to get shaken up. Encourage kids to think of both positive and negative events. As kids say each event, swirl/shake the bottle so glitter is disturbed.

- Negative events: fighting with a sibling or schoolmate, losing a game, getting a bad grade, sad news on the TV, natural disasters
- Positive events: doing well on a test, winning a sports game, visiting a relative, making a new friend, accomplishing something (riding a bike, etc.)

Remember it can take a few minutes to calm the brain after the amygdala is activated, just like it takes some time for the glitter in the jar to settle after being shaken. This can be really helpful for those who don't understand why their mind and body may be feeling a certain way. If you think about your thoughts and emotions like the glitter, it makes sense you need a few minutes to calm down before you can begin thinking clearly again.

Stress Activation + Caregiver Comforting
Reflection Questions:
- What is a recent event that raised your heart rate, made you anxious? How did you cope?
- With kid(s), brainstorm healthy habits to reduce stress. Do they find enjoyment out of exercise, playtime, music, board games, or something else?

Practice yourself:
- General Strategies:
  - When confronted with a stressful event, begin by asking, "Why am I stressed?" or "What is bothering me?"
  - If your child is beginning to work themselves up, ask them, "Why are you stressed?" or "What is bothering you?"
  - Just like Maria was able to make Rafael feel safe, you can help to turn off another person's stress response by creating a space for them to process their stressful experience.

73

- Say it out loud: Labeling or naming our worries tells our emotion centers that it is okay to be upset. Children learn directly from their caregivers. As caregivers, you can help teach them that it is okay to be upset.
- Music: Not only is music enjoyable, but it has also been shown to act as a powerful stress reducer. Encouraging children to participate in local music programs is an effective way to teach stress-reducing skills, while also learning a lifelong skill.

Bigger people/protective factors/relational health
Reflection Questions:
- What are ways *you* can look to strengthen your relationships with friends and family?
- What are things that older, safe humans can do to make younger humans feel safe?

Common knowledge... or not?
1. Myth: Brain development only happens in children and young adults.
   Fact: The brain is constantly learning and incorporating new information, even in adulthood.

2. Myth: Strong attachment relationships between child and caregiver do not have an effect after childhood.
   Fact: Strong attachment relationships, established by responsive and attentive caregiving, are protective factors against mental illness in the future and predict increased cognitive abilities.

Activities:
- Cooperation Games: **The single most influential protection against stress is personal relationships.** Seek out games that promote teamwork and cooperation. Group activities such as team tag, brainstorming solutions to an everyday problem, or playing board games with a partner will help to

show kids that when adversity or hardship enters their life, they will overcome the difficulties by leaning on their friends, families, and teachers. *One thing that can be extremely helpful in buffering stress is to have an adult or an older safe person help the child to process the event.*

Technology and the Brain
Reflection Questions:
- In what ways is your child's screen time replacing more important activities?
- Are there ways that you could use in-person activities to think deeper about what you watch on a screen? For example...
  - You could watch a movie with animals one day, and then go to the zoo the next day
  - Make a movie instead of watching one
  - Play video games that limit to a certain number or time limit per day
  - Use automated screen time limits
  - Encourage interactive educational games

Tug of War: Dopamine/Oxytocin Systems
Reflection Questions:
- What types of things, situations, or experiences usually make you feel like there is a tug of war going on inside your brain?
- When you're feeling this tug of war, how do you decide what to do?

Activities:
- When working with kids, *remember that there are a lot of things competing for their attention and motivation.* Try to help them think through decisions such as the tug of war that Rafael encounters.
- *Provide many opportunities for children to interact with their peers.* The reward pathway in the brain is activated by

75

many things, from social media to television to social acceptance. It is important to help children regulate their response to reward, so that they don't always choose screen time to displace social time.

- *Be conscious of technology use.* Technology is not entirely bad. However, as a caregiver it is important to not overly rely on technology. As much as possible, consider questions such as: what is this technology replacing? Are there other activities we could be doing together?

Footprints in the Snow/Learning

Reflection Questions:
- What daily activities do children participate in that provide them the skills to do harder tasks later in life?
- What types of things are hard or confusing at first to learn, but then become second nature?

Common Knowledge...or not?
- <u>Myth</u>: The best way for children to learn is through a strict curriculum of activities and assignments.
  <u>Fact</u>: The best way for children to learn is through interactions with peers and caregivers/adults and their environment. Children should be encouraged to explore their own interests, and caregivers can participate in that with them.

Mirror Neurons and Empathy

Reflection Questions:
- What early experiences have informed your resilience? Do you and your immediate friends/family feel comfortable communicating with each other?
- When is the last time someone stood up for you?

Common Knowledge...or not?
<u>Myth</u>: Attachment bonds are only important in infancy and early childhood.

<u>Fact:</u> ALL individuals, regardless of age, need to feel close to other humans. Our brains expect there to be others around us who can comfort us and help us deal with stressful situations, even as adults.

Activities:
- As you are working with a child, regularly ask them questions such as, *what are you seeing? Do you know what that person is doing? What do you think will happen next?* Questions like these will prompt kids to reflect on what they are seeing to help practice new skills.

Healthy Habits
Reflection Questions:
- What are some easy health habits you can think of?
  - How can you add these healthy habits into your daily routine?
- What old habits is your brain holding on to? Do these old habits get in the way of new healthy habits?

Here are some examples of healthy habits for your own life and your child's life:
- Giving your child a hug and telling them you love them every morning
- Making a healthy breakfast
- No electronics at the dinner table
- Going for a family walk and talking about your day
- A bedtime routine (example: turning off screens at a certain time, taking a bath, and reading a book together every night)

Executive Functioning
Reflection Questions:
- Ask children about times they have been flexible, learned a new skill at school, or had to react calmly when they

disagreed with a friend. Even without realizing it, children are constantly practicing executive functioning.

- Are there ways you can involve children in your daily activities? Even making small plans or to-do lists can help teach a child how to stay organized.

Ways to enhance Executive Functioning:
- <u>Yoga</u> - yoga has been found to promote executive functioning and learning!
- <u>Charades</u> - when children engage in pretend play, they work on important skills such as knowing their own role in a story. These are easy ways to encourage complex levels of thinking

Learning as a lifestyle: When kids are exposed to an enriched life full of interesting discussions, like family trips to the zoo, museum, or even a snowball fight, learning is emphasized in all aspects of life, not just the classroom.

About the Authors:

Rebecca Hammond, Alex Nisbet, and Kate Brown began writing this book during their senior year of college at the University of Notre Dame. They hope that readers will be able to learn about their brains and develop healthy habits formed in love.

About the Illustrator:

Olivia Schenck is a first-year neuroscience major at the University of Notre Dame. All four years in high school, she played lacrosse and ran cross country. She believes that there is art in healing and loves building community relationships and resilience through her art.